SNOW PATROL
EYES OPEN

© 2006 by Faber Music Ltd
First published by Faber Music Ltd in 2006
3 Queen Square, London WC1N 3AU

Art direction by Mat Maitland with Richard Andrews at Big Active.
Images by Mat Maitland.
Photography by Dan Tobin Smith.
Studio photography by Bradley Quinn

Arranged by Alex Davis & Tom Fleming
Engraved by Camden Music
Edited by Lucy Holliday & Olly Weeks

Printed in England by Caligraving Ltd

ISBN 0-571-52717-5

To buy Faber Music publications or to find out about the full range of titles available,
please contact your local music retailer or Faber Music sales enquiries:

Faber Music Ltd, Burnt Mill, Elizabeth Way, Harlow, CM20 2HX England
Tel: +44(0)1279 82 89 82 Fax: +44(0)1279 82 89 83
sales@fabermusic.com fabermusic.com

YOU'RE ALL I HAVE

Words and Music by Gary Lightbody, Nathan Connolly, Jonathan Quinn, Paul Wilson and Tom Simpson

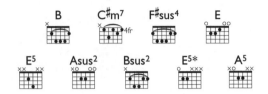

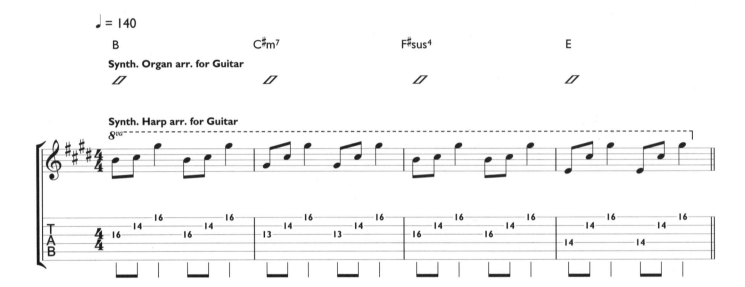

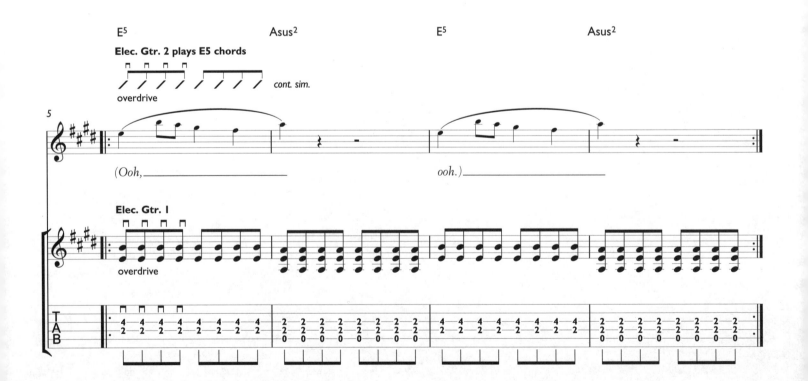

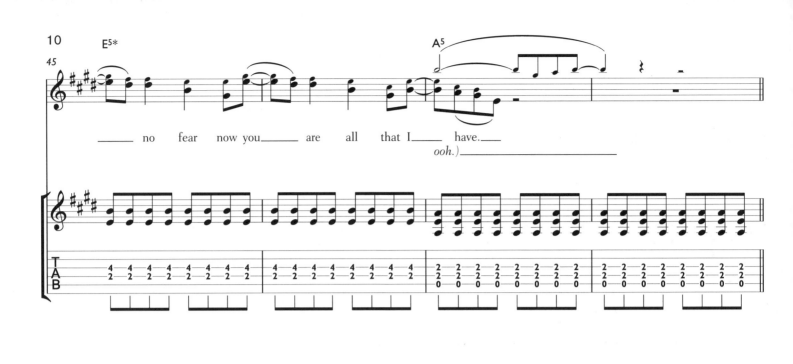

no fear now you___ are all that I___ have.___
(ooh.)___

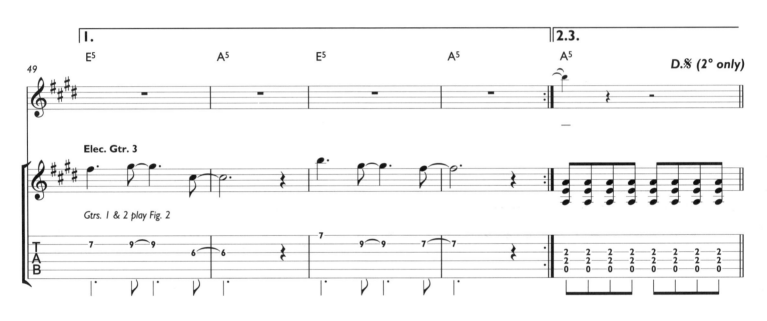

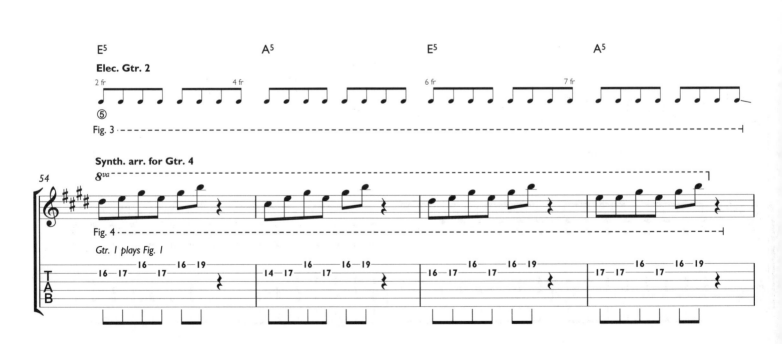

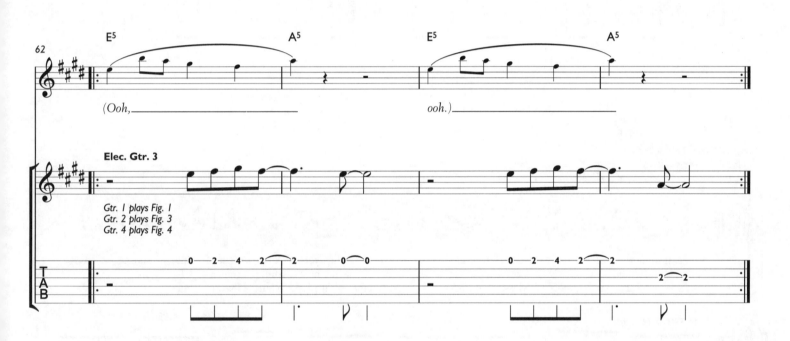

HANDS OPEN

Words and Music by Gary Lightbody, Nathan Connolly, Jonathan Quinn, Paul Wilson and Tom Simpson

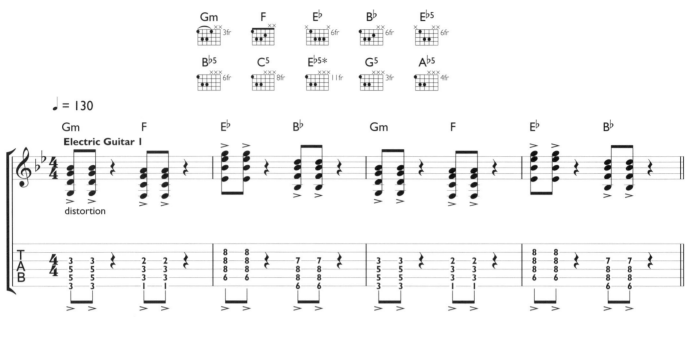

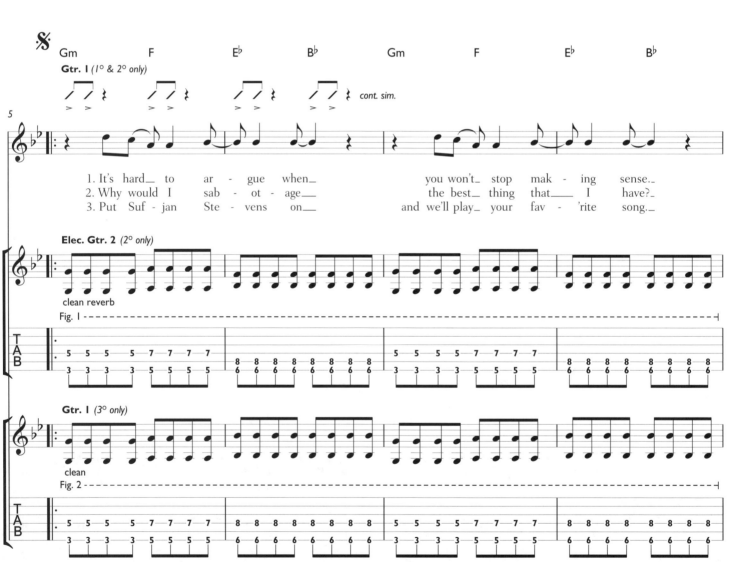

1. It's hard to ar - gue when you won't stop mak - ing sense.
2. Why would I sab - ot - age the best thing that I have?
3. Put Suf - jan Ste - vens on and we'll play your fav - 'rite song.

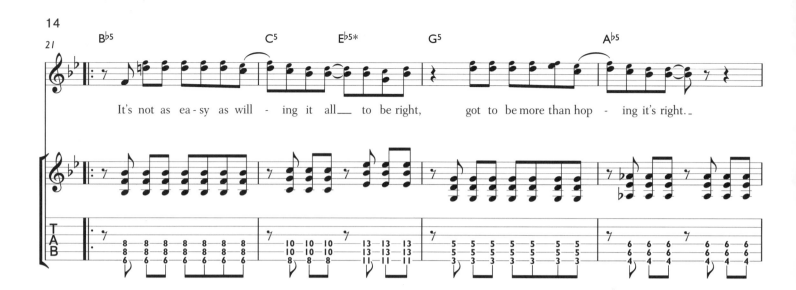

It's not as ea-sy as will - ing it all__ to be right, got to be more than hop - ing it's right.__

D.% al Coda

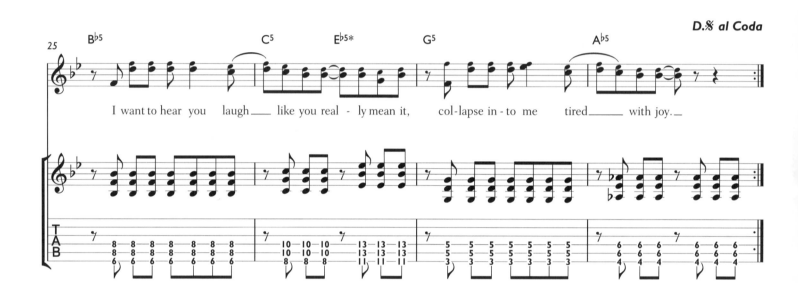

I want to hear you laugh__ like you real - ly mean it, col-lapse in-to me tired____ with joy.__

⊕ *Coda*

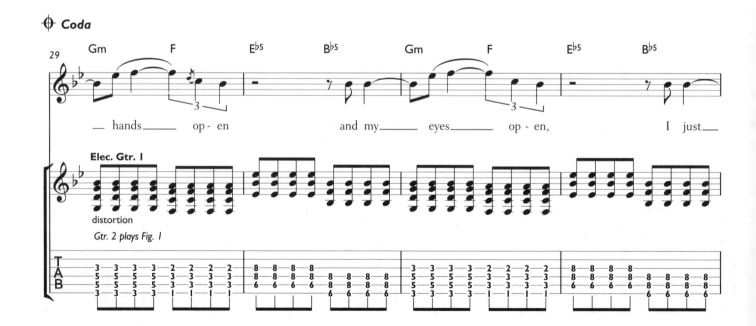

__ hands____ op - en and my____ eyes____ op - en, I just__

Elec. Gtr. 1

distortion

Gtr. 2 plays Fig. 1

CHASING CARS

Words and Music by Gary Lightbody, Nathan Connolly, Jonathan Quinn, Paul Wilson and Tom Simpson

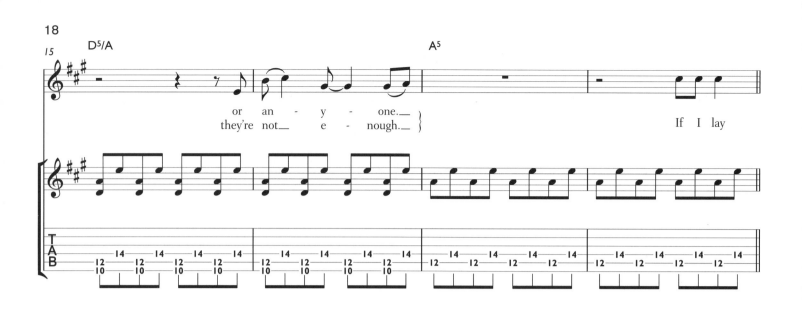

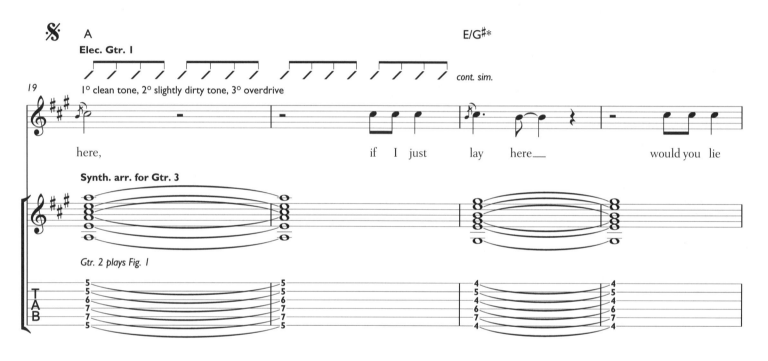

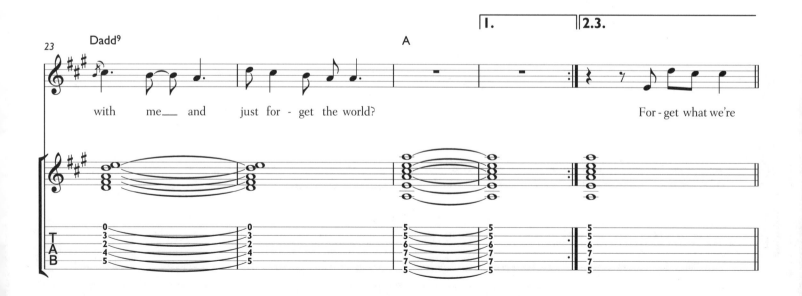

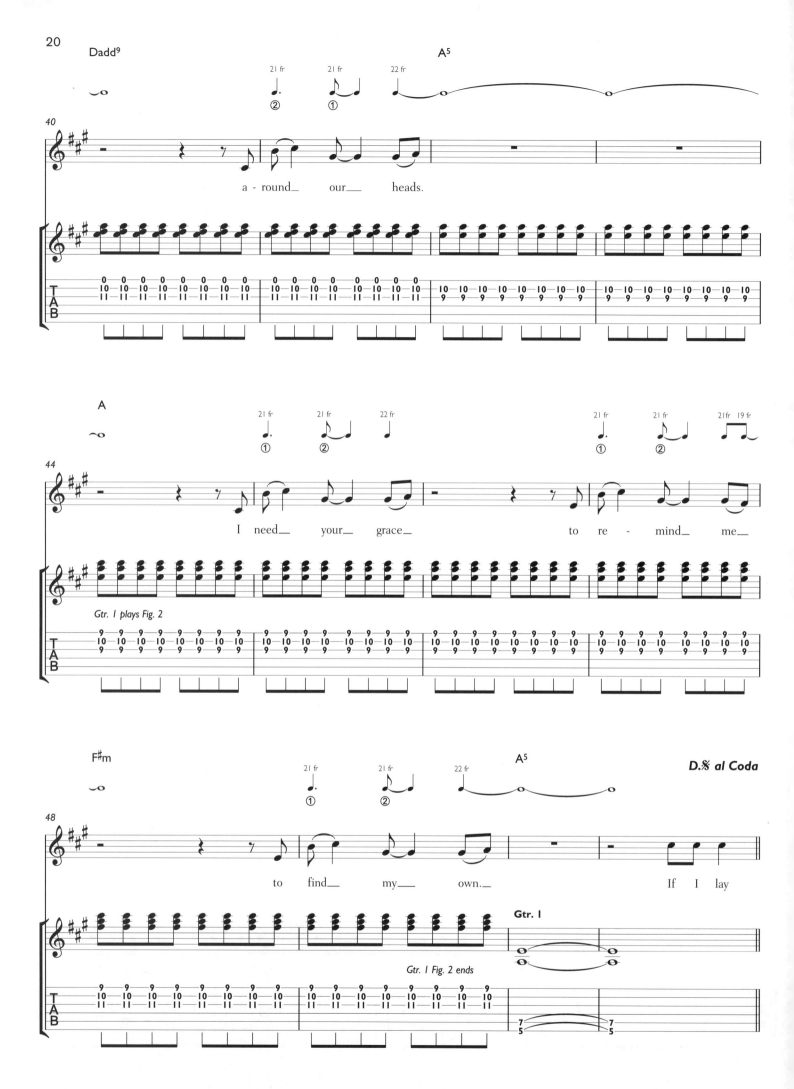

SHUT YOUR EYES

Words and Music by Gary Lightbody, Nathan Connolly, Jonathan Quinn, Paul Wilson and Tom Simpson

just close your eyes_ un - til_____ you can i - mag-ine this place, yeah our___ sec - ret space at will._

Gtr. 3 plays Fig. 2 (1° only)

Gtr. 1 & Bass play Fig. 1
Gtr. 2 plays Fig. 3

(Shut your eyes,___ shut your eyes.)___

Elec. Piano arr. for Gtr. 2

Gtr. 1

IT'S BEGINNING TO GET TO ME

Words and Music by Gary Lightbody, Nathan Connolly, Jonathan Quinn, Paul Wilson and Tom Simpson

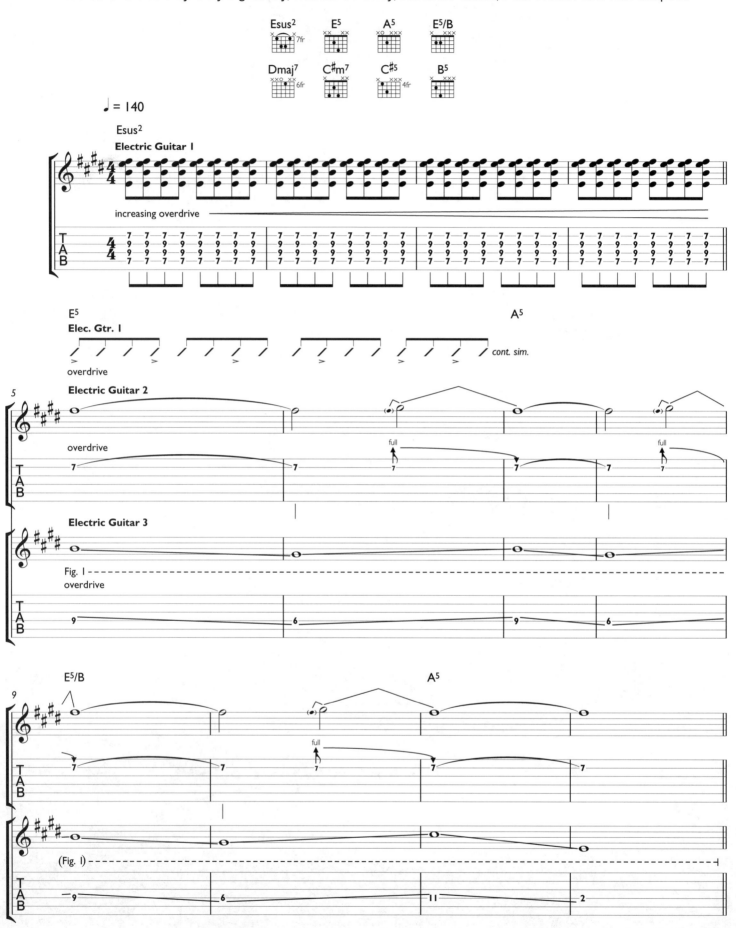

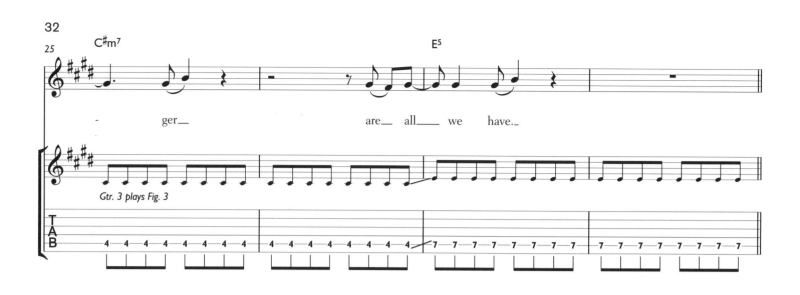

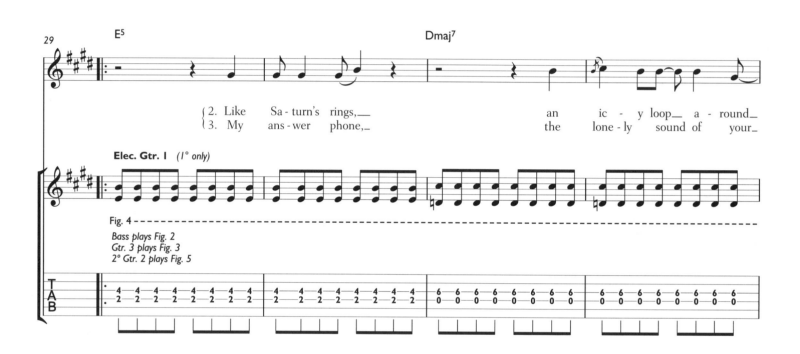

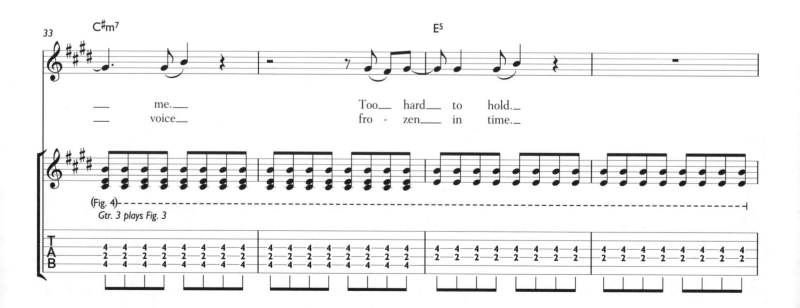

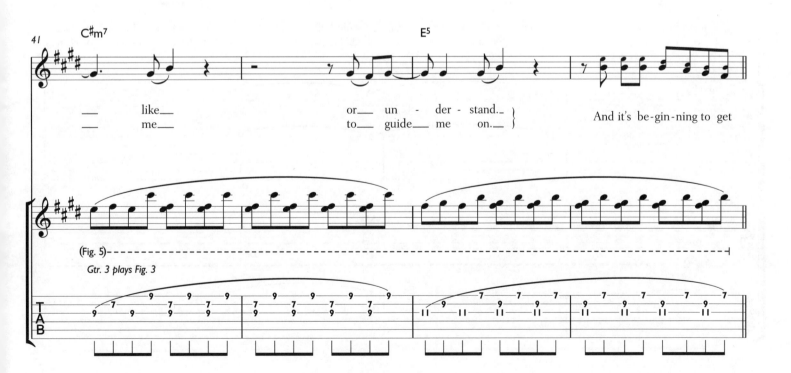

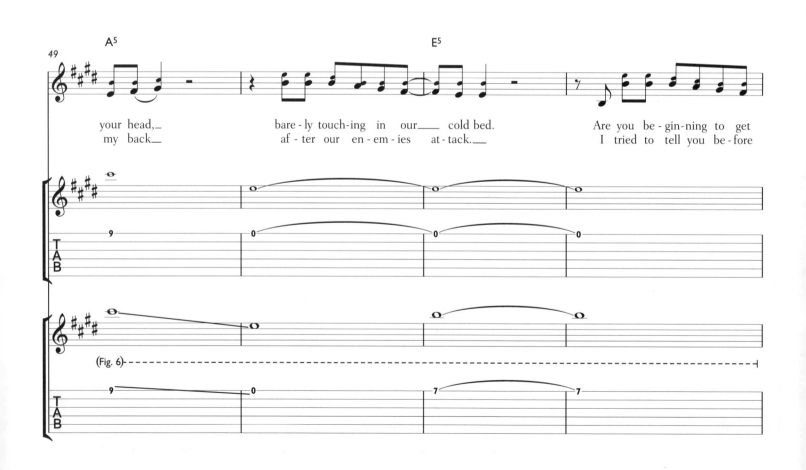

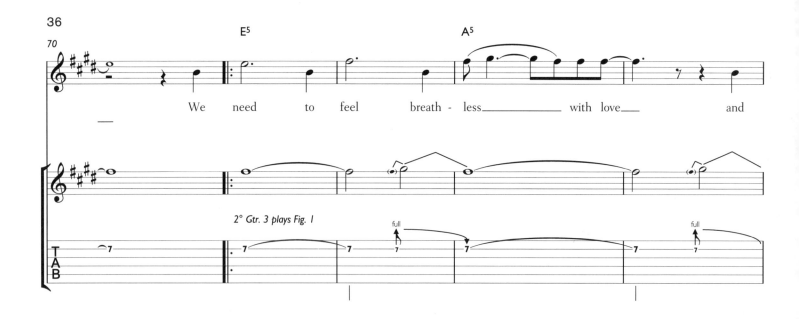

We need to feel breath - less_____ with love_____ and

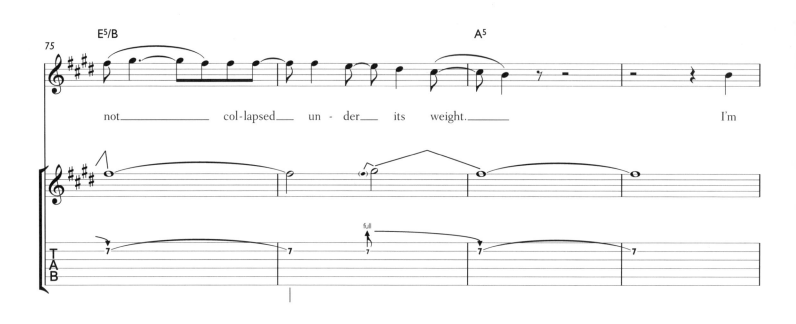

not_____ col-lapsed_____ un - der_____ its weight._____ I'm

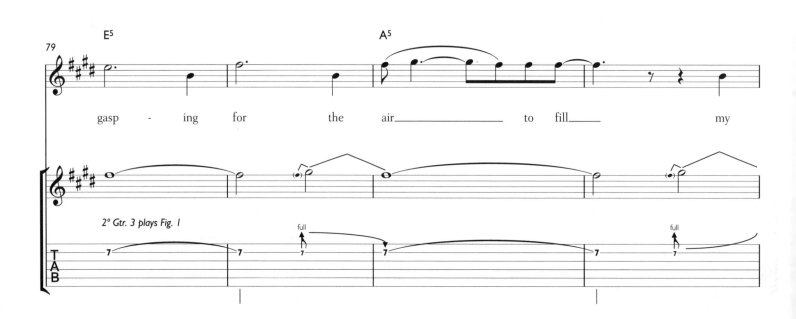

gasp - ing for the air_____ to fill_____ my

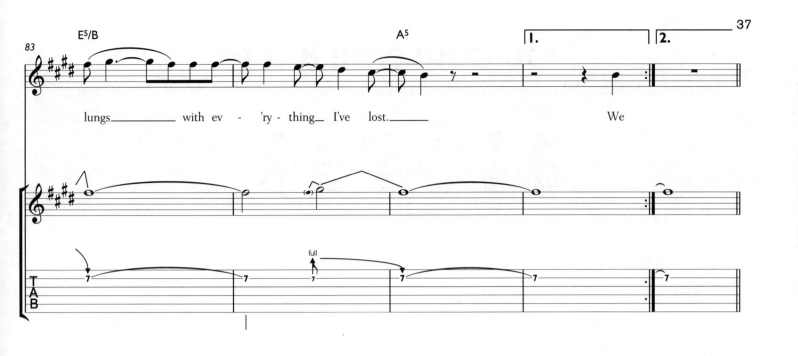

lungs_____ with ev - 'ry - thing__ I've lost._____   We

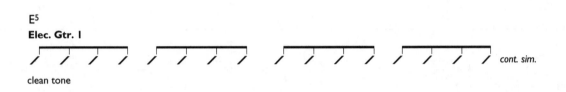

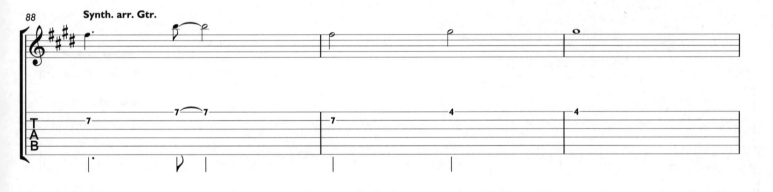

YOU COULD BE HAPPY

Words and Music by Gary Lightbody, Nathan Connolly, Jonathan Quinn, Paul Wilson and Tom Simpson

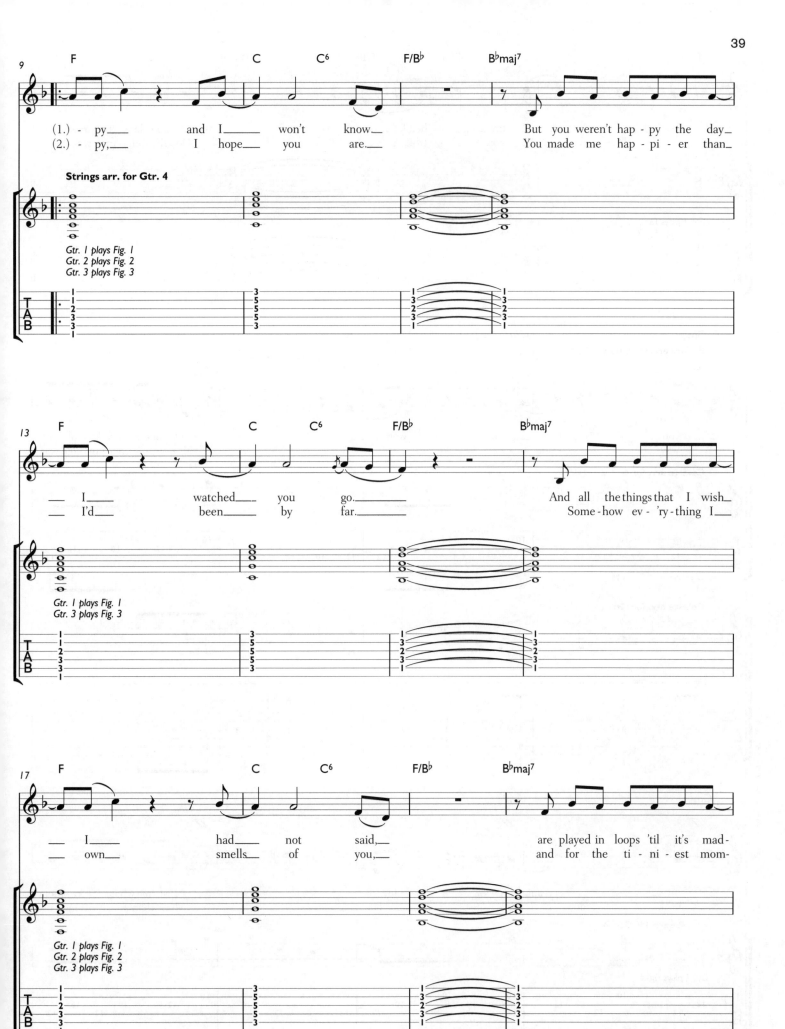

MAKE THIS GO ON FOREVER

Words and Music by Gary Lightbody, Nathan Connolly, Jonathan Quinn, Paul Wilson and Tom Simpson

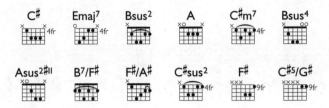

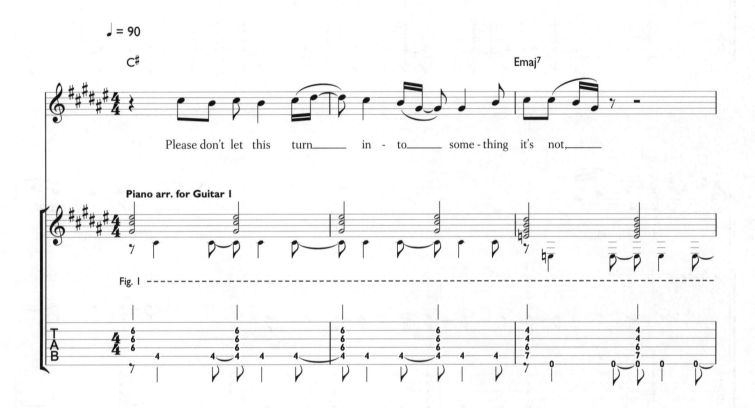

Please don't let this turn____ in - to____ some - thing it's not,____

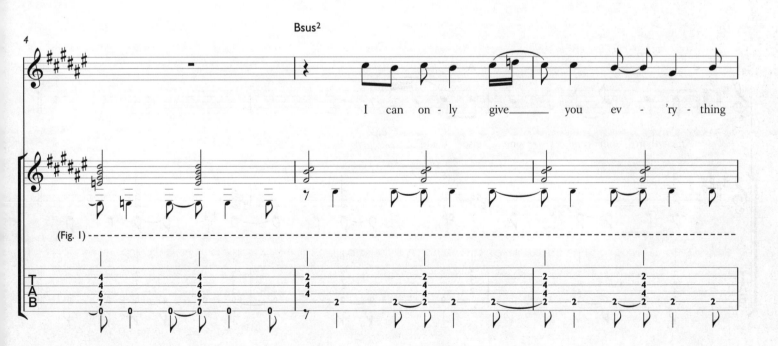

I can on - ly give____ you ev - 'ry - thing

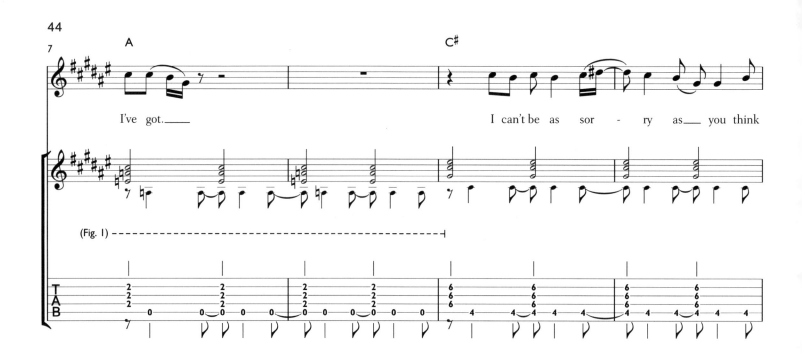

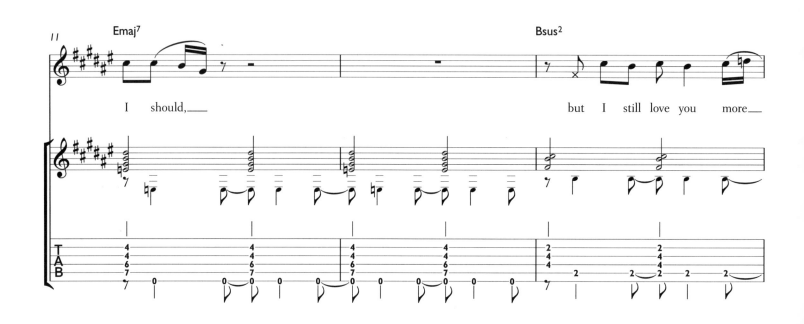

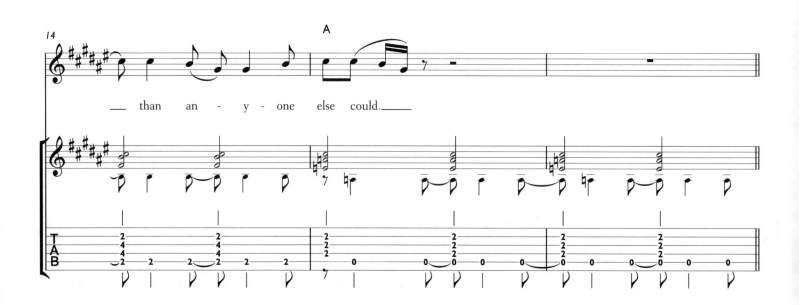

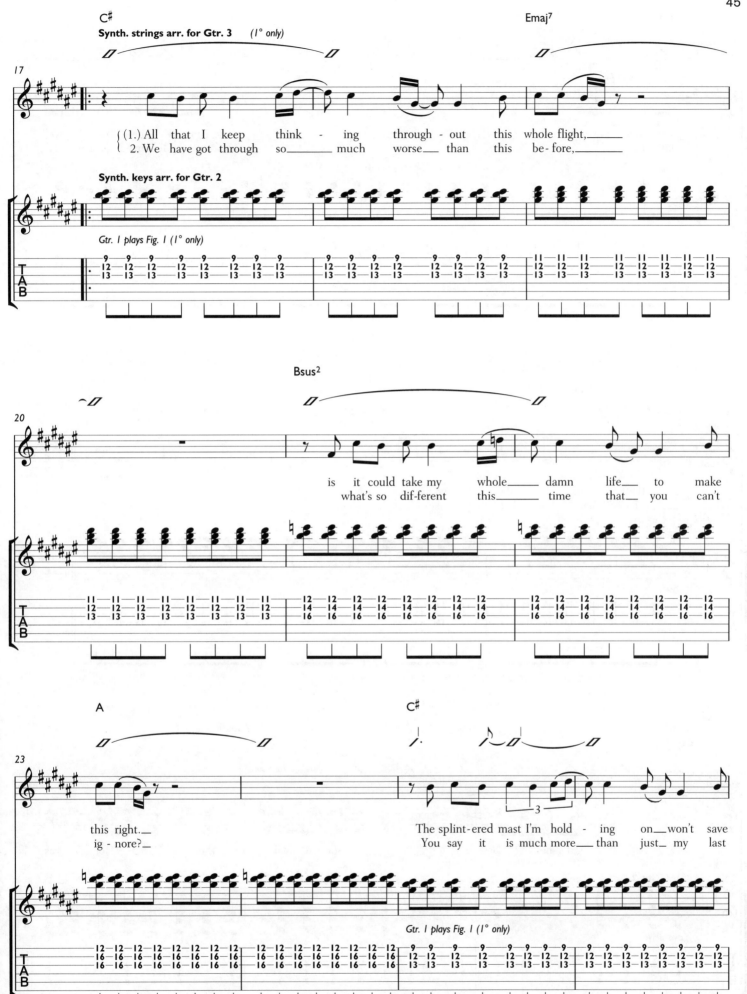

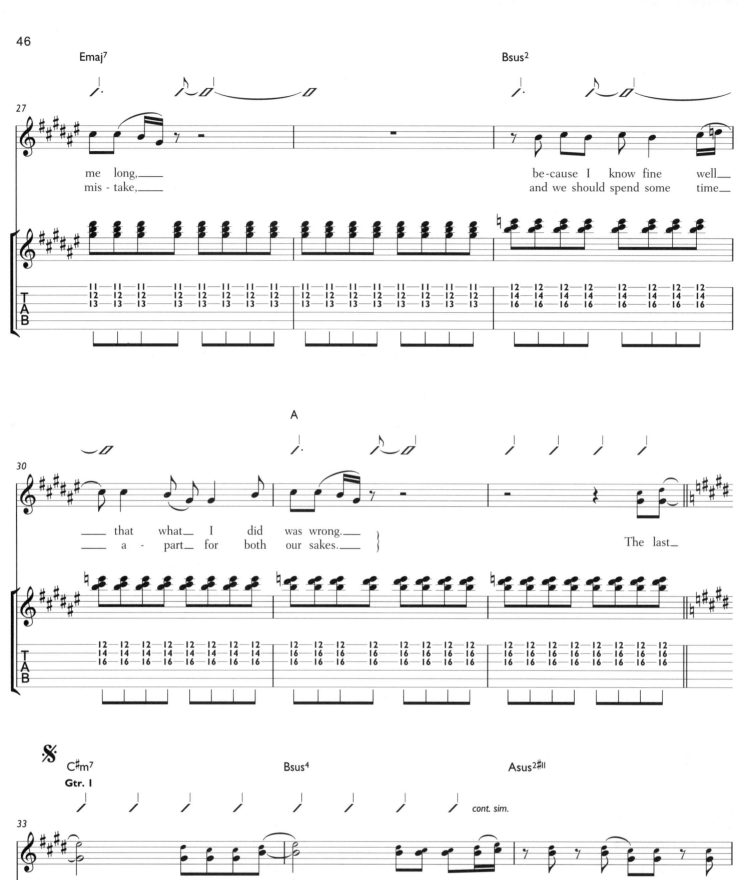

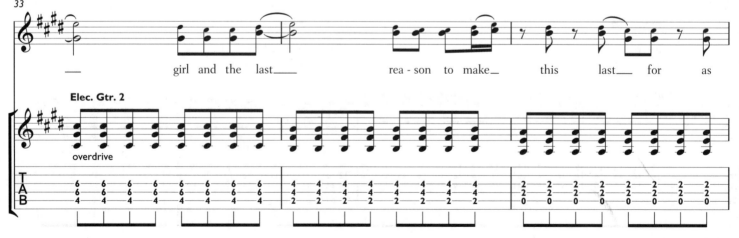

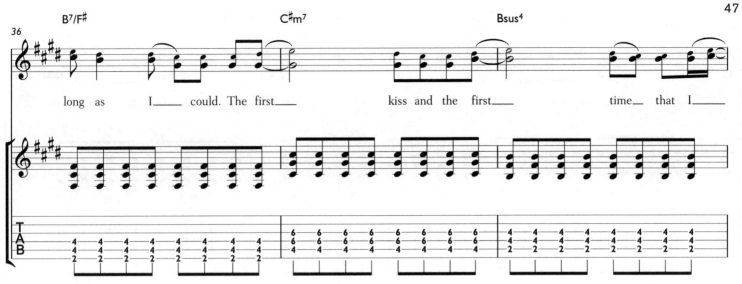

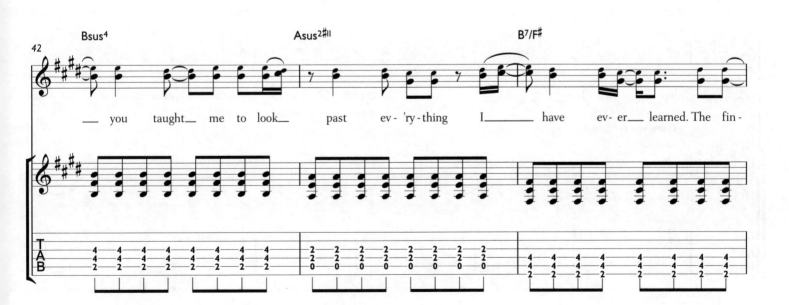

al word in the fin - al sen-tence you ev - er ut - tered to me___

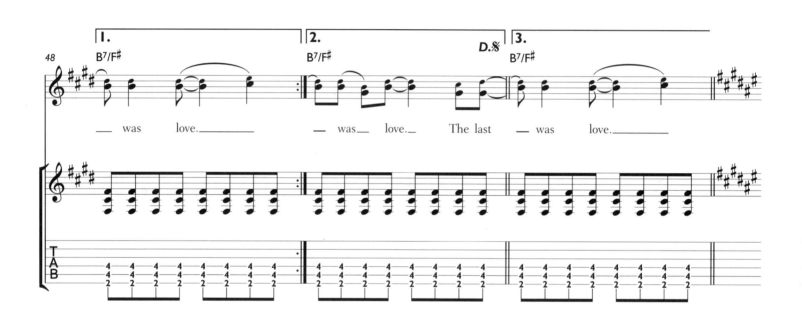

___ was love.___   ___ was___ love.___   The last ___ was   love.___

where   to look.   My words   just   break   and melt.

Please just save me from this dark - ness,_ please just save me from this

dark - ness._ And I don't know

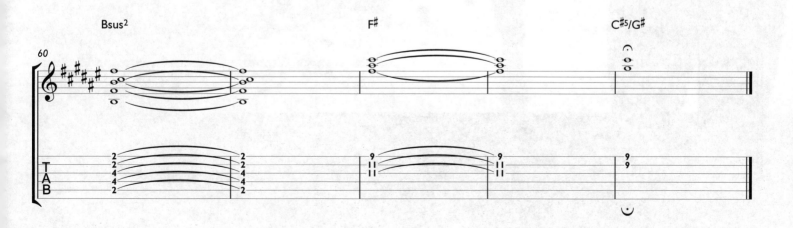

SET THE FIRE TO THE THIRD BAR

Words and Music by Gary Lightbody, Nathan Connolly, Jonathan Quinn, Paul Wilson and Tom Simpson

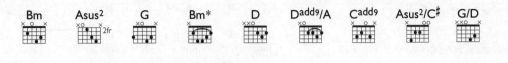

(Male & female vocals)

1. I find the map____ and draw a straight line, over riv - ers, farms and state lines.
2. I hang my coat____ up in the first bar, there is no peace____ that I've found so far.

The dis - tance from____ a to where you'd b, it's on - ly fing - men
The laugh - ter pen - e - trates my si - lence, as drunk - en men

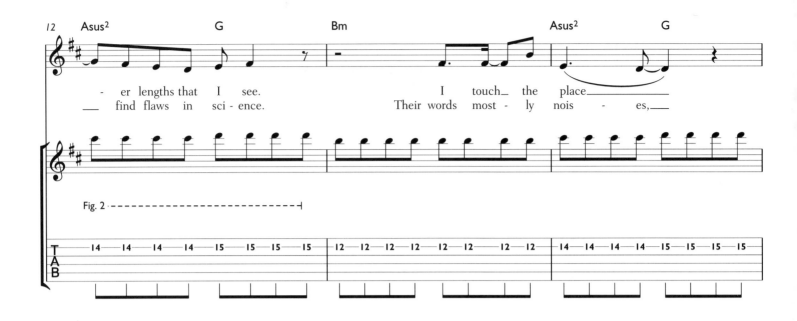

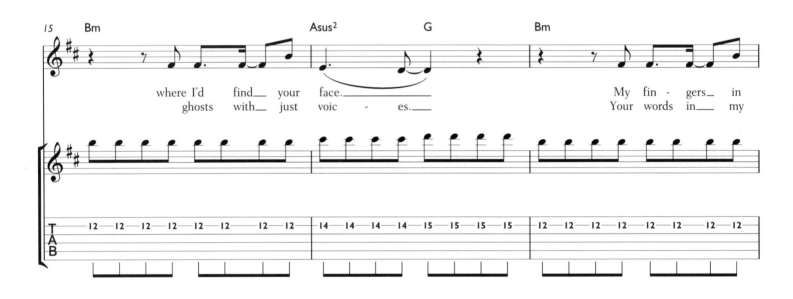

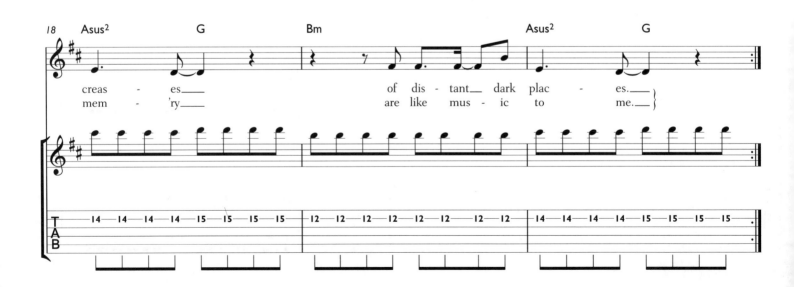

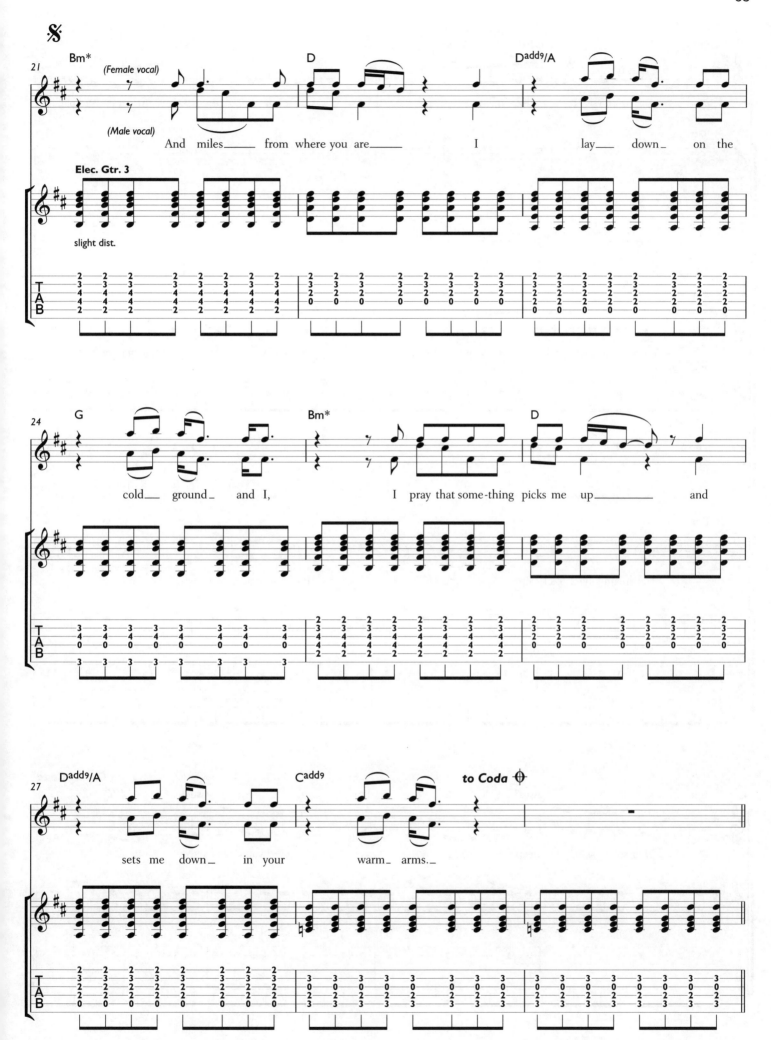

⊕ **Coda**

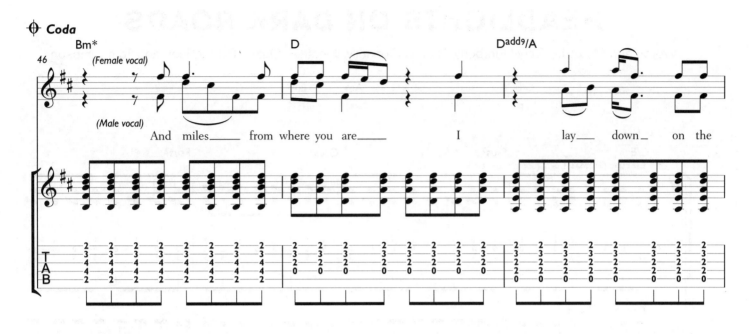

And miles____ from where you are____ I lay____ down_ on the

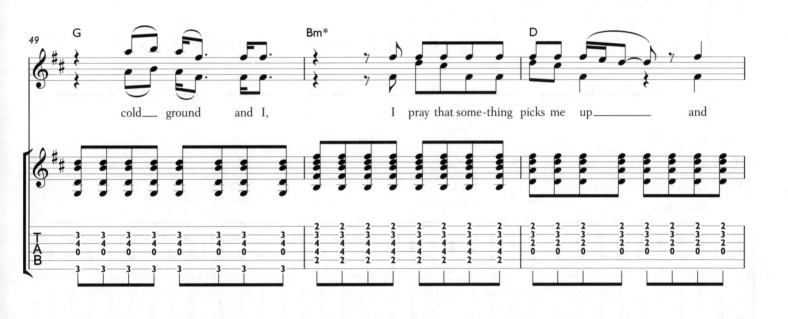

cold__ ground and I, I pray that some-thing picks me up_____ and

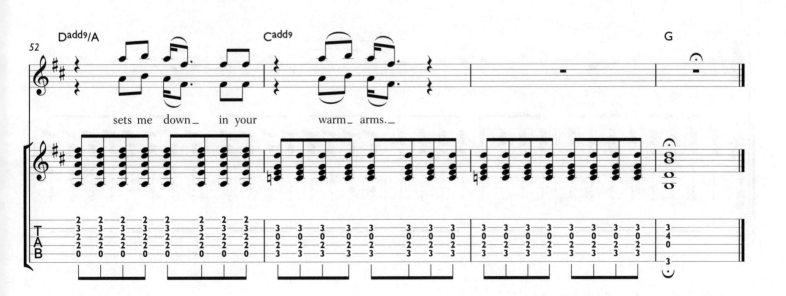

sets me down_ in your warm_ arms._

HEADLIGHTS ON DARK ROADS

Words and Music by Gary Lightbody, Nathan Connolly, Jonathan Quinn, Paul Wilson and Tom Simpson

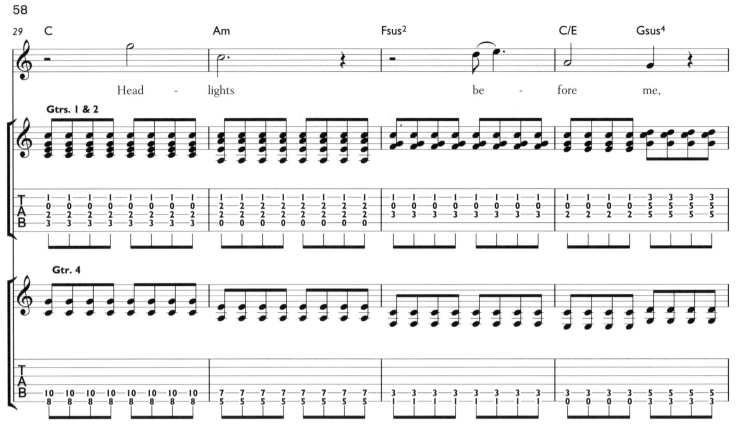

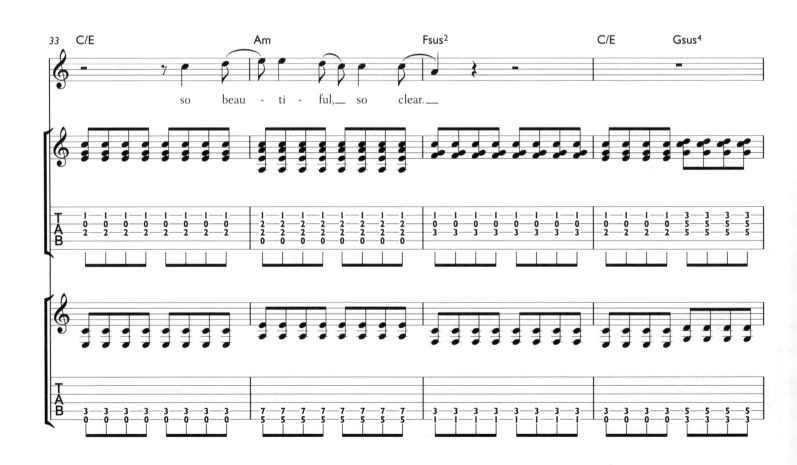

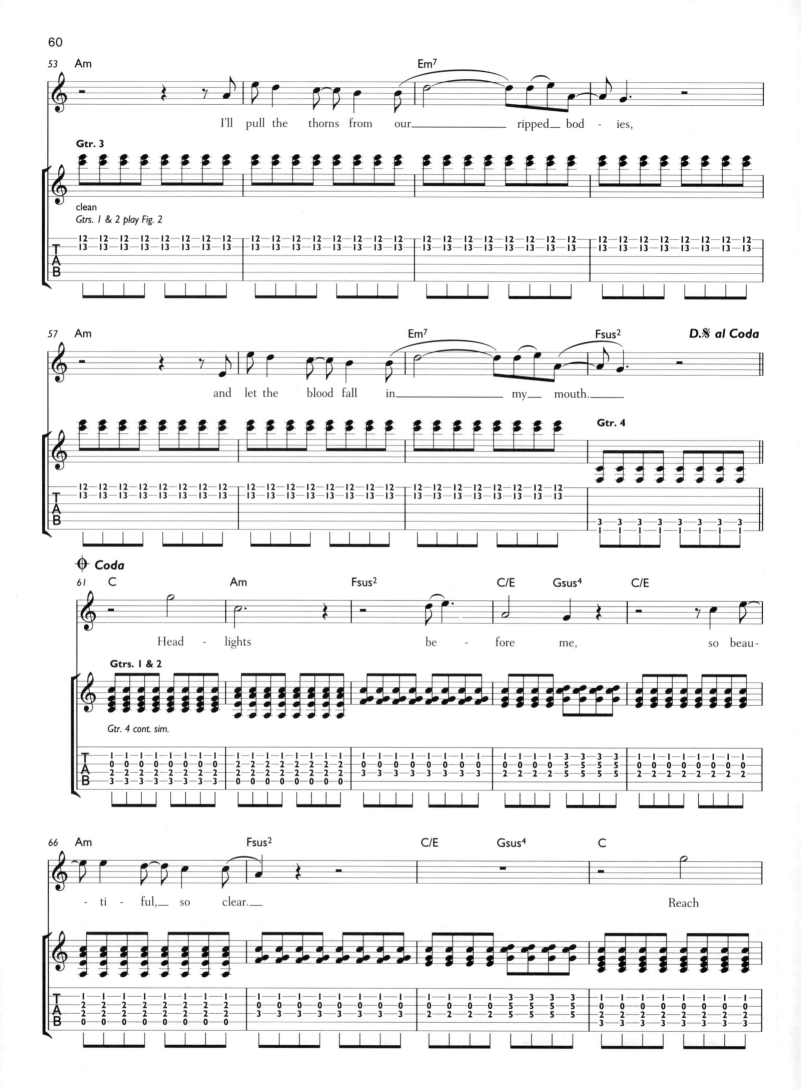

OPEN YOUR EYES

Words and Music by Gary Lightbody, Nathan Connolly, Jonathan Quinn, Paul Wilson and Tom Simpson

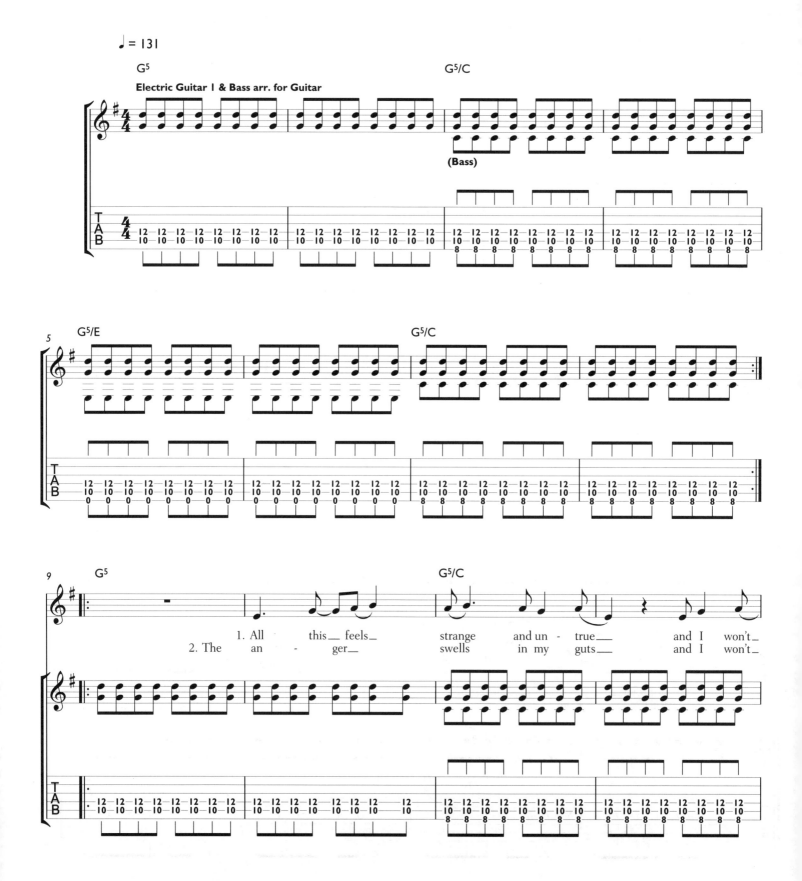

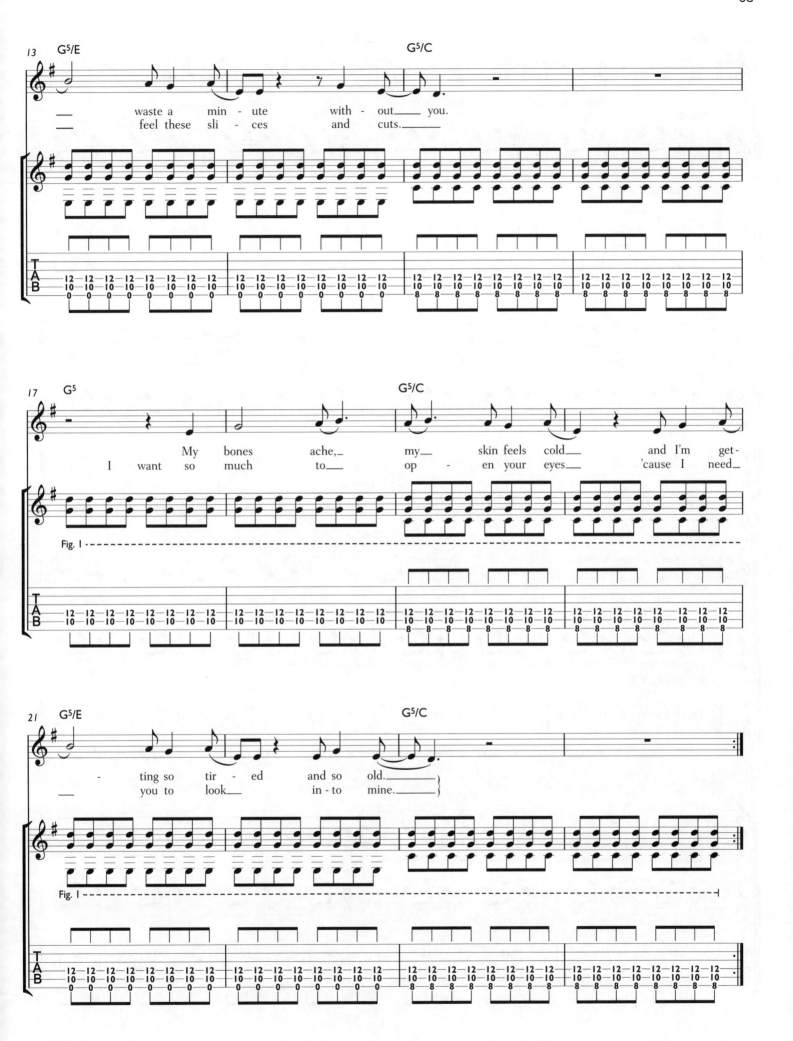

Take my hand, knot your fin - gers through mine___ and we'll walk
I want so much to___ o - pen your eyes___ 'cause I need___

___ from this dark___ room for the last___ time.
___ you to look___ in - to mine.___

Fig. 2 ------------------

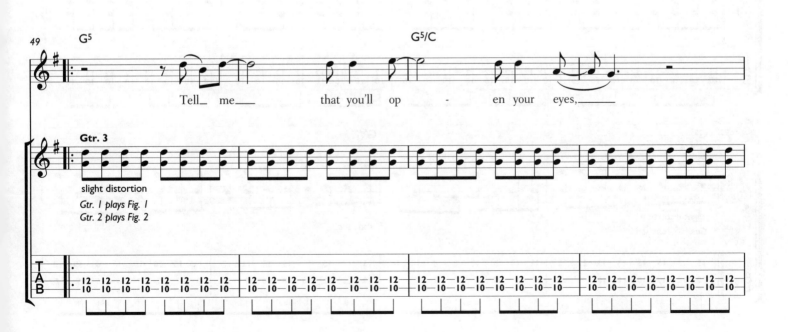

Tell___ me___ that you'll op - en your eyes,___

Gtr. 3
slight distortion
Gtr. 1 plays Fig. 1
Gtr. 2 plays Fig. 2

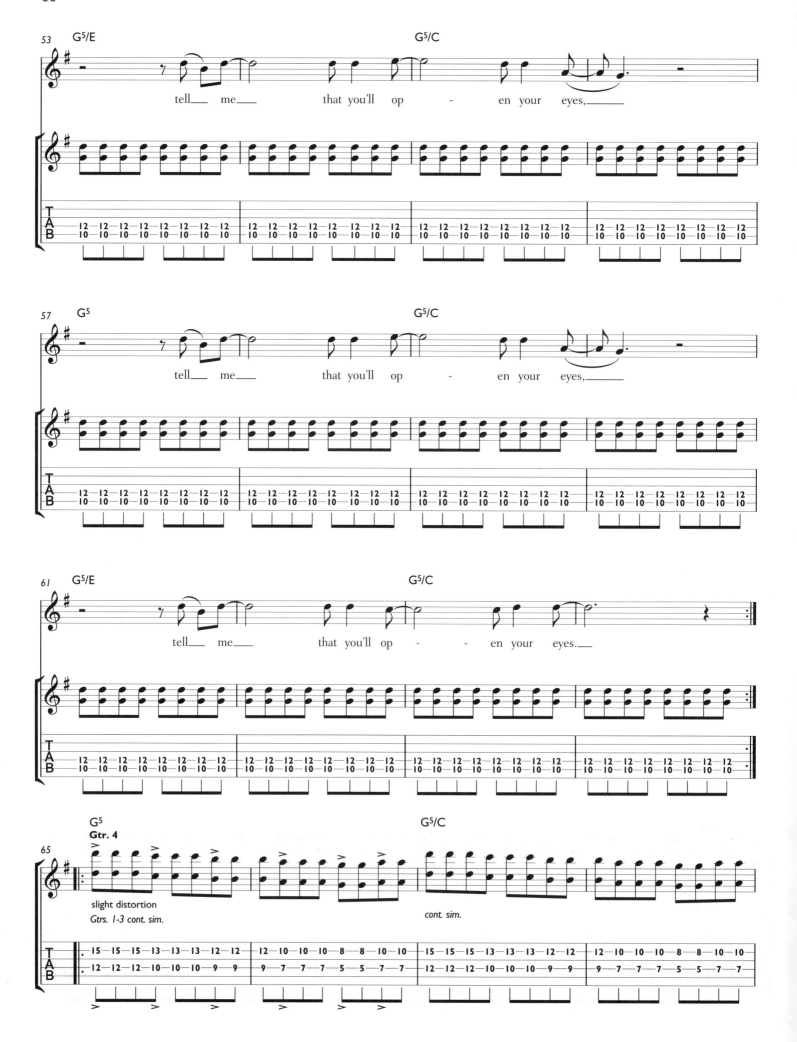

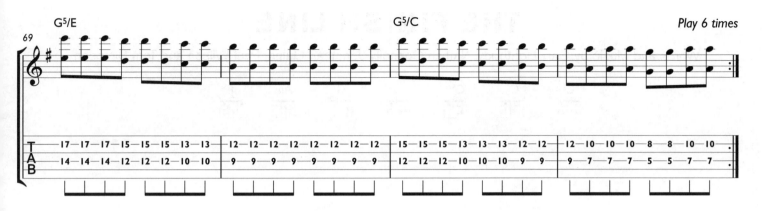

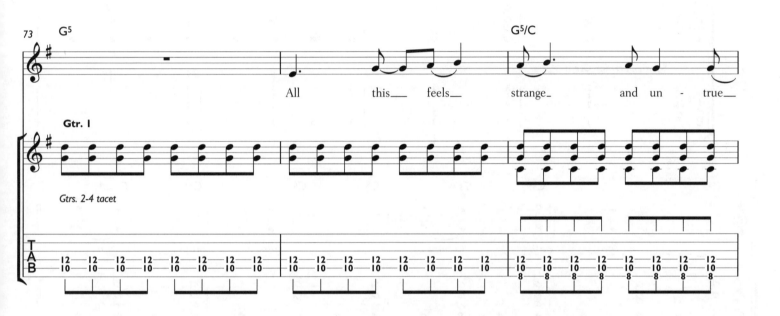

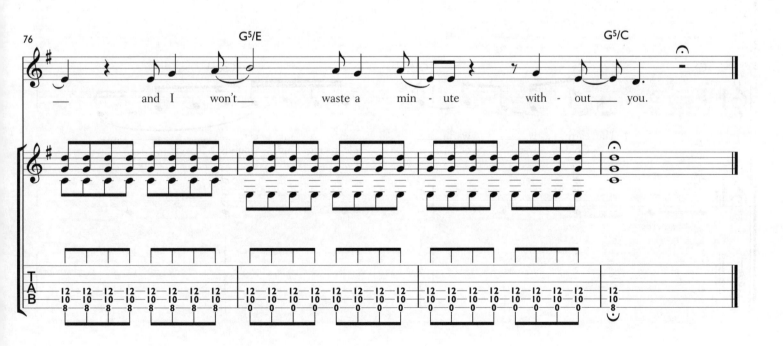

THE FINISH LINE

Words and Music by Gary Lightbody, Nathan Connolly, Jonathan Quinn, Paul Wilson and Tom Simpson

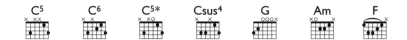

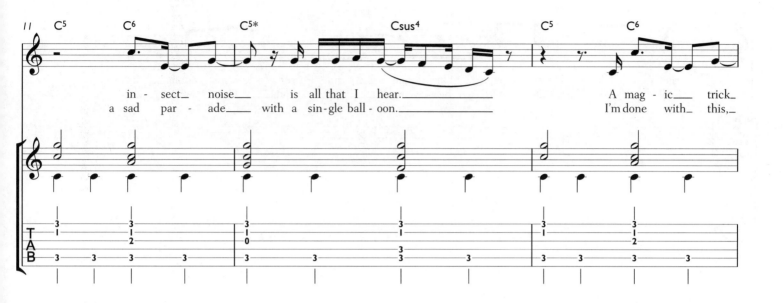

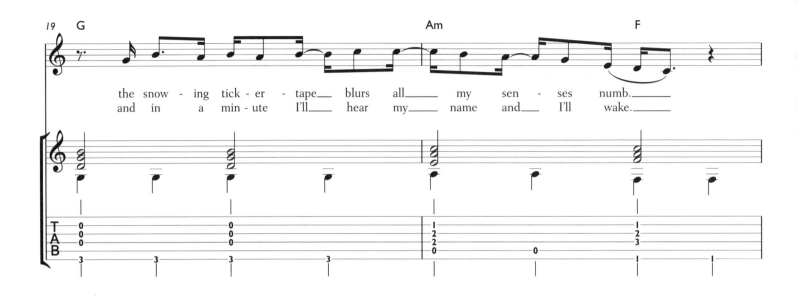

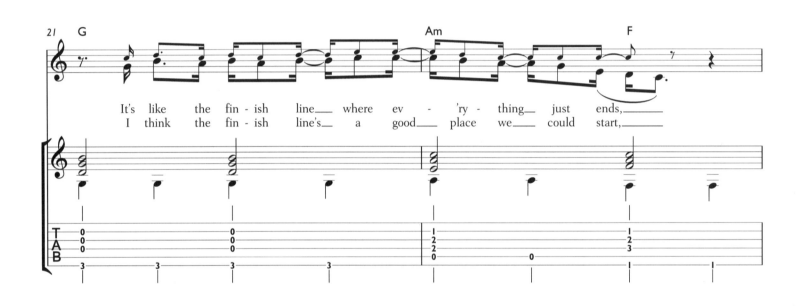

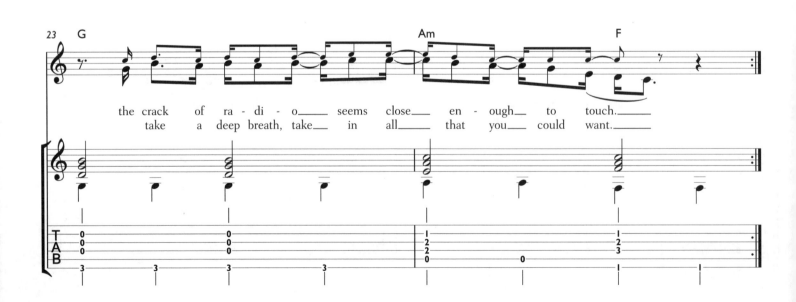

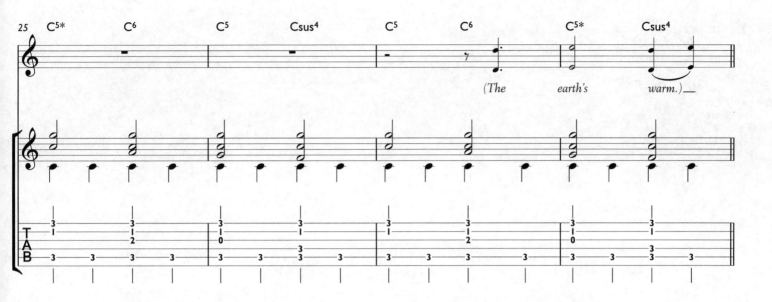

(The earth's warm.) __

Piano arr. for Gtr. 2

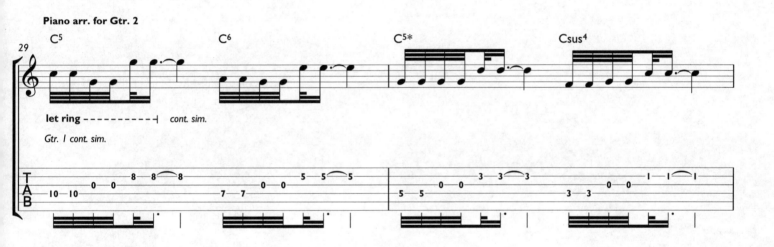

let ring ---------- cont. sim.

Gtr. I cont. sim.

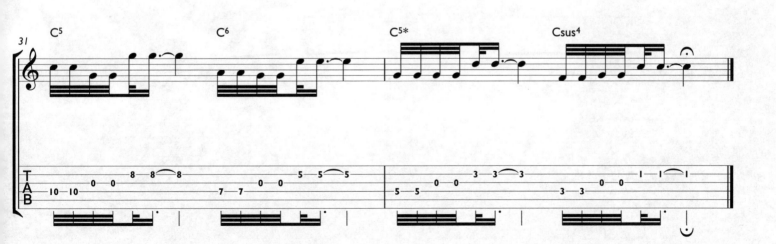

IN MY ARMS

Words and Music by Gary Lightbody, Nathan Connolly, Jonathan Quinn, Paul Wilson and Tom Simpson

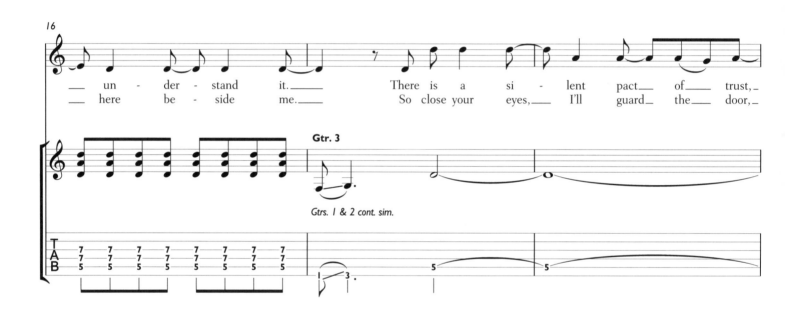

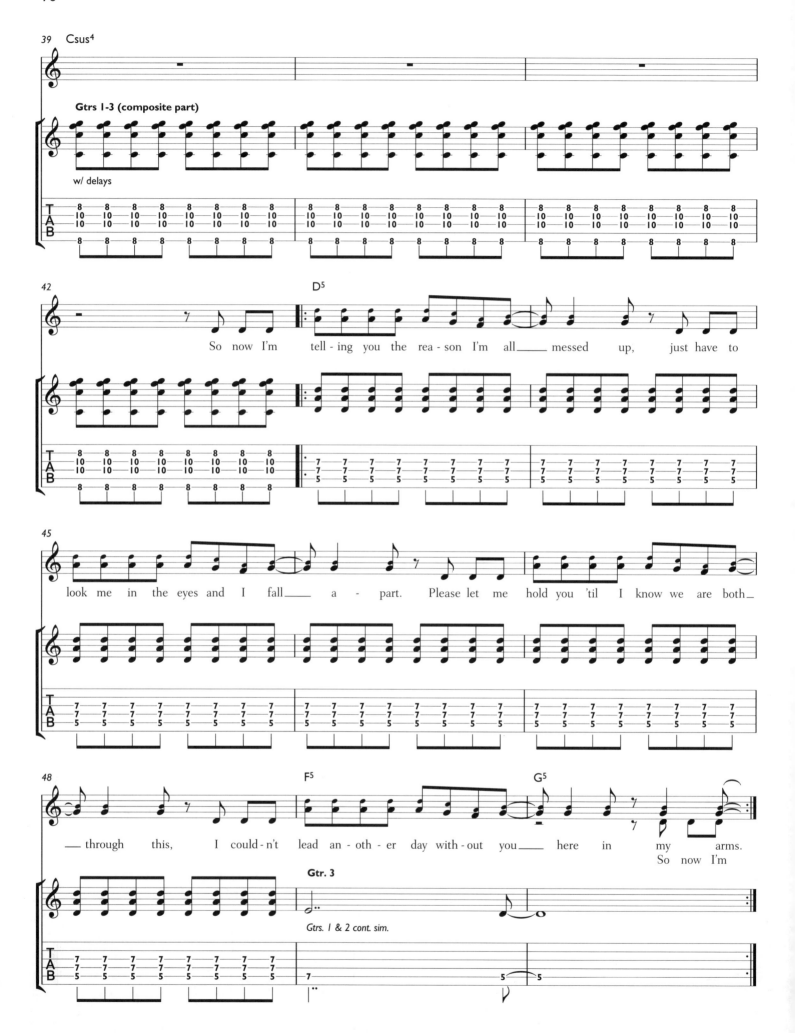

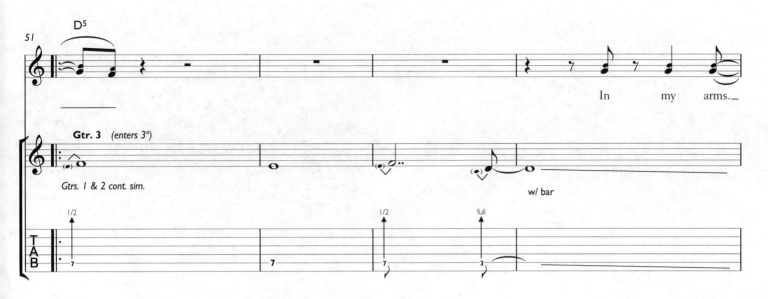

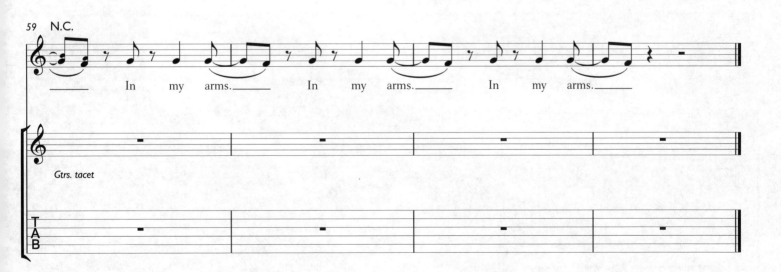

WARMER CLIMATE

Words and Music by Gary Lightbody, Nathan Connolly, Jonathan Quinn, Paul Wilson and Tom Simpson

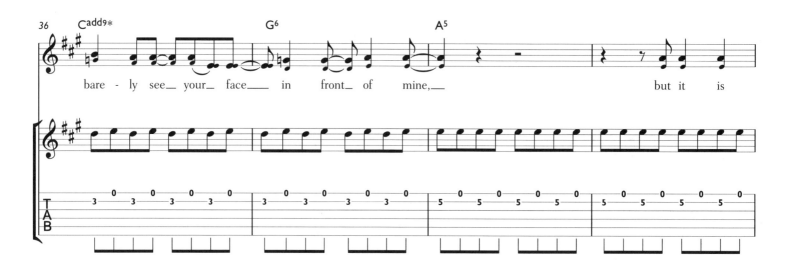

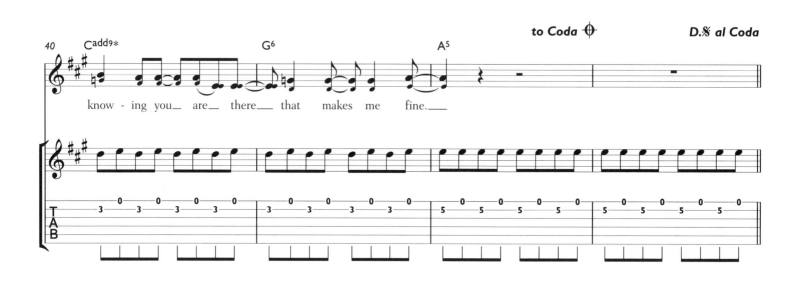

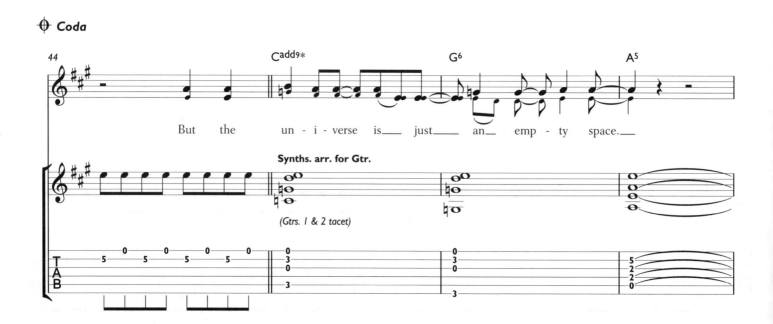

And all the stars can dis - ap - pear___ with - out___ a trace.___ I'm so

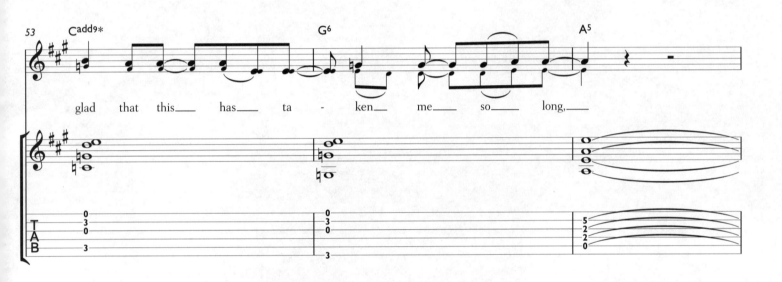

glad that this___ has___ ta - ken___ me so___ long,___

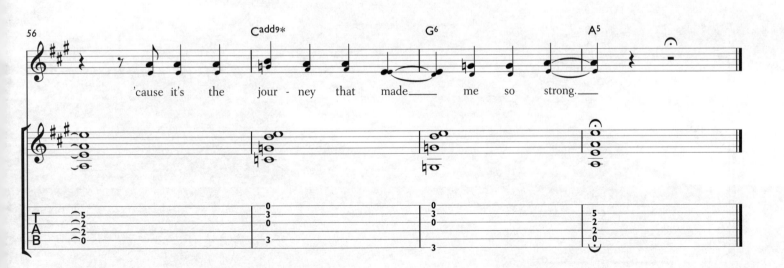

'cause it's the jour - ney that made___ me so strong.___